What's Wrong with Me?

What happens when you're ill;
and ways to stay healthy

J e n n y   B r y a n

Illustrations by Martin Shovel

Wayland

Editor: Katrina Maitland Smith
Senior Editor: Cath Senker
Designer: Simon Balley and Jean Wheeler
Consultant: Dr Tony Smith

First published in 1994 by Wayland (Publishers) Ltd
61 Western Road, Hove, East Sussex BN3 1JD, England

British Library Cataloguing in Publication Data

Bryan, Jenny
What's Wrong with Me?
I. Title
613.0432

ISBN 0 7502 1114 8

Typeset by Vanessa Good and Jean Wheeler
Printed and bound in Italy by
G. Canale & C.S.p.A., Turin

Picture acknowledgements
The publishers would like to thank the following for permission to use their photographs in this book: Chapel Studios (John Heinrich) 17; Trevor Hill 27; National Medical Slide Bank 20; Science Photo Library (John Durham) 9, 15, (Blair Seitz) 16; Wayland Picture Library 4, 11 (both), 22, 24; ZEFA 6, 12, 18.

Cover and illustrations by Martin Shovel.

Contents

I don't feel well

What do you do when you feel ill? You can tell your mum or dad, your teacher or someone who looks after you. Adults can only help you if you can say what is wrong. They may ask you some questions.

Have you got a pain?
Where does it hurt?
Do you feel sick?
Do you feel hot?
When did you start feeling ill?

Think carefully. The more you can tell them, the better.

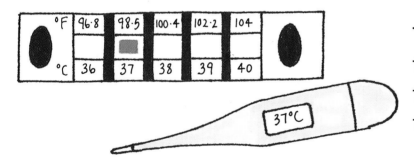

They may also take your temperature using a thermometer like one of those pictured here.

The normal temperature of your body is 37°C (98.5°F). If you are feeling hot, you may have a higher temperature because your body is fighting an infection.

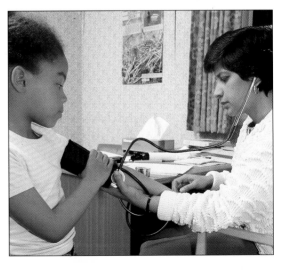

If you see a doctor, he or she will ask you questions, too. The doctor may look into your mouth or ears or listen to your chest to try to find out what is wrong.

Sometimes you may need to go to hospital to see another doctor who knows a lot about certain illnesses or parts of the body. When they know what is wrong, the doctors can tell you what to do to get better.

Your body

Some of the most important parts inside your body are your brain, your heart, lungs, kidneys and your liver.

Your brain is where you think and decide what to do. It is also in charge of most of your movements.

Your heart is a big pump. It pushes blood all around your body through lots of small tubes. Your lungs are full of air. Your body needs oxygen, which it takes from the air in your lungs. The oxygen is carried around your body in your blood.

Your liver helps to change the foods you eat into substances your body needs for energy and to grow. Your kidneys help to remove substances which you don't need in your body.

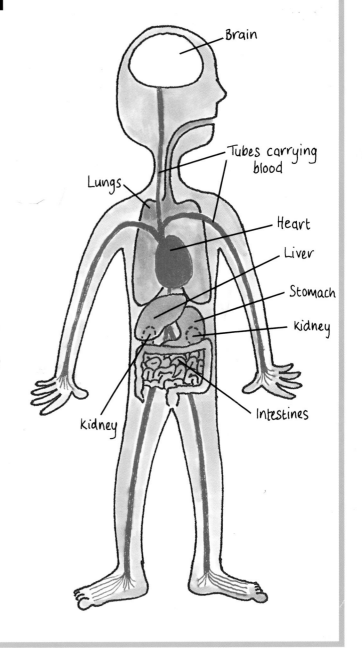

Brain
Tubes carrying blood
Lungs
Heart
Liver
Stomach
Kidney
Intestines
kidney

I have a cough

All sorts of things can make you cough.
Food may go down the wrong way. You
may cough when you go into a smoky
room. If you catch a cold, your throat
may be sore and red and you may cough
up sticky stuff called phlegm, or mucus.

*You sometimes cough when you
play outside in a cold wind.*

Your throat

*In your throat there are two tubes.
One takes food down into your
stomach. The other takes air to your
lungs. The air tube has a flap like a
lid which usually stops food going
down into your lungs when you
swallow. Sometimes food can slip
past the lid, perhaps because you
are eating too fast, so you cough to
make the food come up again.*

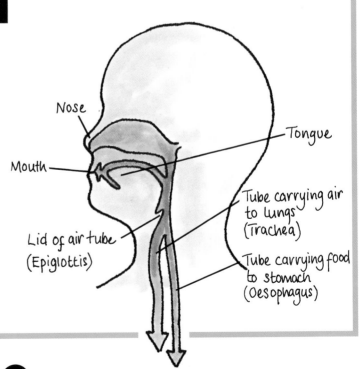

Nose

Mouth

Tongue

Lid of air tube
(Epiglottis)

Tube carrying air
to lungs
(Trachea)

Tube carrying food
to stomach
(Oesophagus)

It's normal to cough when something upsets your throat or lungs. It's your body's way of trying to get rid of it.

Help yourself

When you eat, be sure to chew your food well. Don't eat quickly or while you are moving around.

Stay out of smoky rooms. If someone in your family smokes, ask them to think about stopping. It's very bad for them and bad for you too. Cigarettes have poisons in them which will hurt your lungs.

You cannot keep away from all the things that cause coughs. Cough medicine may help to make your throat feel better, but you should only take medicines that are given to you by someone who looks after you.

I'm sneezing

You sneeze when something makes the inside of your nose itch. Dust or pollen, for example, can get right up your nose! You cannot scratch so you just have to sneeze.

People sneeze more than usual when they have a cold. Tiny microbes in the air cause colds. They are called cold viruses. You cannot see them but they are always around. They get up your nose and into your throat.

It is important to cover your mouth when you sneeze or cough. If you don't, and you have a cold, the viruses could travel through the air to give someone else a cold.

A virus can make your eyes and nose sore and your nose swollen and full of mucus. It may make your throat sore and make you feel hot. If the mucus gets in your throat, you will cough as well.

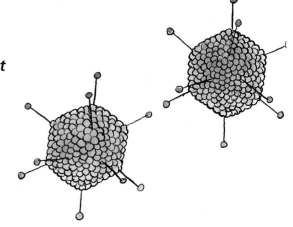

Pollen grains (left) are so tiny that you can only see what they look like through a microscope. Viruses, like those that cause sore throats and colds (right), are even smaller.

Some people always seem to have a cold. Their noses run a lot and they often have itchy and watery eyes. Their noses and eyes are upset by things like dust and pollen that float around in the air. This may mean that they have hayfever, or allergic rhinitis.

SCIENCE BOX

Allergies

Your body may be upset by some things that don't affect other people, such as animal fur, dust and pollen. These things may make you sneeze, wheeze, or give you a rash on your skin because your body is fighting them like an infection. This is called an allergy. Hayfever and allergic rhinitis are allergies.

Help yourself

There is no cure for a cold. Your body will produce things called antibodies to fight the viruses. It usually takes about four or five days to kill them all. You may be given medicine to make you feel better.

If you have allergic rhinitis, you can have tests done to find out which things upset your nose and eyes. If, for example, animal fur makes you sneeze, try not to touch animals.

I have a toothache

Toothache hurts a lot. You can get it if you don't look after your teeth and gums.

Your teeth are living things, just like the rest of your body. They have an outer coating to protect them. It's called enamel. If you let food stay on your teeth, bacteria will come and live on them, feeding on the sugar in the food. Bacteria make acid and this will attack the enamel on your teeth and make holes in it.

Then the acid will get inside your teeth and destroy them too. This is called tooth decay and it gives you toothache.

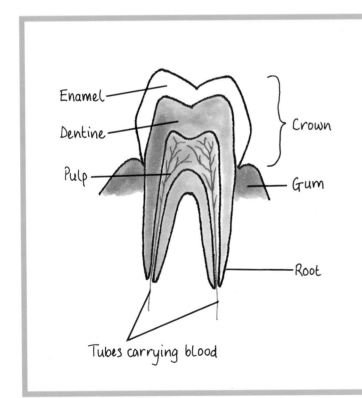

Enamel

Dentine

Pulp

Crown

Gum

Root

Tubes carrying blood

SCIENCE BOX

Your teeth

The part of a tooth which we can see sticking out of the gum is called the crown. Inside the gum, each tooth has a long root to hold it in place. A tooth has three layers. The enamel on the outside is the hardest substance in your body. Beneath the enamel is another hard substance called dentine. This surrounds a layer of pulp which contains nerves and tiny tubes carrying blood.

Help yourself

You won't get toothache if you keep your teeth very clean. You should brush them carefully at least twice a day, after breakfast and before you go to bed.

Make sure you brush all your teeth – the back ones and the front ones, on the inside as well as the outside. Ask your dentist to show you how to clean your teeth properly.

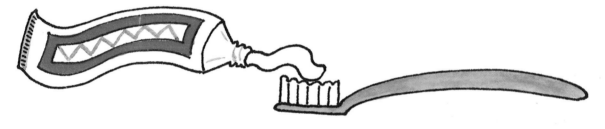

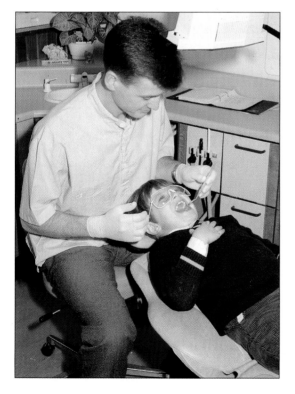

Use a toothpaste which has fluoride in it. This will help keep your teeth strong. And don't eat too many sweet things.

If you get toothache, go to the dentist as soon as you can. If you have a hole in a tooth, the dentist will clean it and fill it so that the bacteria cannot get in to make it bigger.

Even if you don't have toothache, go to the dentist every six months to make sure your teeth are healthy.

I've got stomach ache

Sometimes your stomach hurts. You may also be sick or have diarrhoea. This may mean that you have eaten food that has gone bad. Harmful microbes grow on bad food. If they get into your stomach they can make you ill.

Sometimes you can see or smell that food is bad. Always throw it away. Sometimes you cannot see that food is bad but the label might tell you the date by which the food should have been eaten. If that date has passed, throw the food away.

All food should be kept in a cool, dry place. Some foods need to be kept in the fridge.

Help yourself

If you do eat something that makes you ill, do not eat anything else until you feel better. Drink lots of water.

When you feel better, do not eat a big meal straight away. First, try something simple like soup and bread without butter and see how you feel.

Sometimes you can get stomach ache simply because you have eaten too much. Try not to eat too many rich, sweet foods.

Eating

When you eat, food goes down a tube in your throat to your stomach. Your stomach is like a bag where food is broken down. Then the food moves down a tube many metres long. This is your intestine. In the intestine, all the goodness is taken out of the food to be used as fuel to make energy for the body and to help it grow. If it was stretched out, your intestine would not fit in your body, but it is coiled around so it takes up less space.

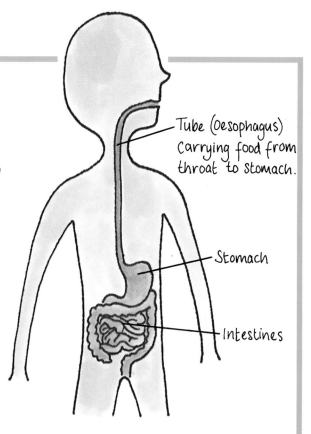

Tube (Oesophagus) carrying food from throat to stomach.

Stomach

Intestines

You may get stomach ache when you are worried about something, like a test or exam. Try to relax and think about something nice. If you have done your work, it will be alright!

I'm wheezy

Do you cough a lot at night or get out of breath quickly when you run about? Listen to the noise you make when you breathe out. Does it sound a bit like a hiss? This is called wheezing. It may mean you have asthma.

Asthma affects your lungs. If you have asthma, air doesn't get in and out of your lungs properly. The tubes that carry the air in and out of your lungs may be too stiff and swollen inside.

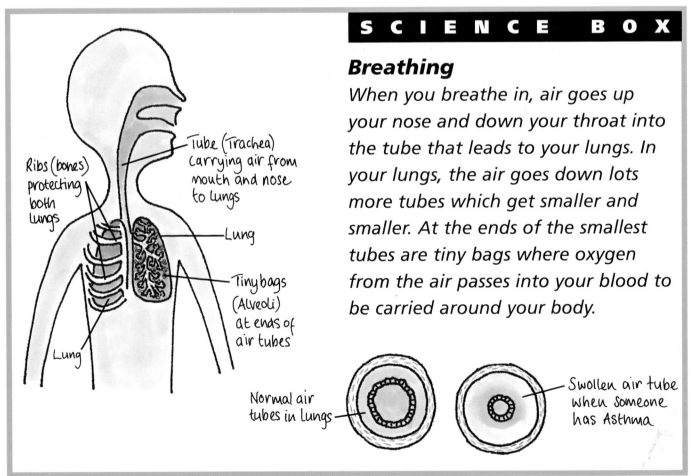

Ribs (bones) protecting both lungs

Tube (Trachea) carrying air from mouth and nose to lungs

Lung

Tiny bags (Alveoli) at ends of air tubes

Lung

Normal air tubes in lungs

Swollen air tube when someone has Asthma

SCIENCE BOX

Breathing

When you breathe in, air goes up your nose and down your throat into the tube that leads to your lungs. In your lungs, the air goes down lots more tubes which get smaller and smaller. At the ends of the smallest tubes are tiny bags where oxygen from the air passes into your blood to be carried around your body.

You'll need to see a doctor. He or she may give you medicines to make the tubes in your lungs less swollen so there is more room for air to get in and out.

The doctor will probably give you an inhaler. Make sure you know how to use it before you leave the doctor. When you are able to use it properly you will be able to breathe more easily. If you have treatment, asthma should not stop you playing games or doing sports.

Help yourself

Pollen, animal fur, feathers, dust and cigarette smoke are some of the things that may make you wheeze (see Science Box on page 9). Keep your bedroom clean and free of dust, and try to keep pets out.

I can't hear properly

Where do you sit in class? At the back or at the front? Can you always hear everything your teachers say to you? If you can't, you should tell them. Or you can tell your mum or dad or someone who looks after you.

Many children do not hear properly because they have had an ear infection. If your ear is painful or feels blocked, you may have an infection that will need treatment. Sometimes, an infection in the ear leaves sticky stuff behind which causes loss of hearing called 'glue ear'.

If you have glue ear, you may need a simple operation (see pages 26–27). A doctor will put a tiny tube in each ear so it does not get blocked again.

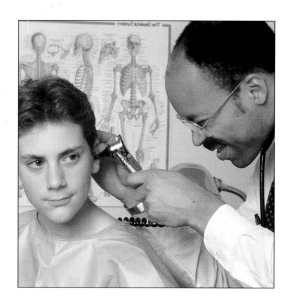

Doctors have special equipment to see inside your ears.

Hearing

Have you ever been in a cave? The inside of your ear looks a bit like that. Sounds go along passageways and through 'caves' until they get to the brain, which tells you what you can hear.

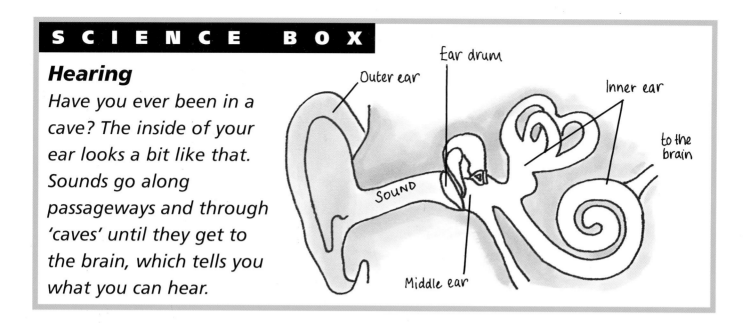

Some children can't hear properly from the time they are born. They may be able to wear a hearing aid in their ear to help them. This makes the sounds around them louder.

Help yourself

Very loud noise or music can hurt your ears or even make you deaf. You should not have your personal stereo so loud that other people can hear it, because this is too loud for your ears.

People who use drills or other machines that make a lot of noise should always wear earmuffs to protect their ears.

I can't see properly

People who can see very well are very lucky! Not many can.

Someone in your family probably wears glasses or contact lenses to help them see better. Some people need glasses to read or drive a car. Others need glasses all the time.

Do you find it difficult to read things on the walls at school? If you do you may need glasses. Why not tell your mum or dad or someone who looks after you. You can have an eye test in which you will probably be asked to read letters off a big chart.

Help yourself
Always look after your eyes. If you hurt them they may not get better. Never put anything sharp near your eyes. Keep away from dangerous machines like saws and drills from which sharp things can fly. People who work with these machines wear goggles to protect their eyes.

If you get anything in your eye, do not rub it. Get help straight away.

Don't look straight at the sun and NEVER look at it through binoculars or a telescope. You will burn your eyes.

If you wear glasses to help you see better, look after these, too. Keep them clean and free of scratches.

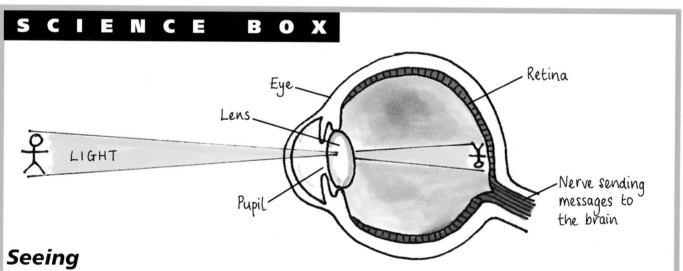

SCIENCE BOX

Labels on the eye diagram: Eye, Lens, Pupil, LIGHT, Retina, Nerve sending messages to the brain

Seeing

We can see because light carries pictures of things into our eyes. Light passes through the little black hole (or pupil) in the front of each eye and makes a picture on the back of the eye.

The picture on the back of the eye is upside down, but messages go from here to the brain which turns the picture the right way up and tells you what you are seeing.

I keep scratching

It's very hard not to scratch when your skin itches, but scratching makes it worse.

Lots of things make your skin itch. You could have an infection. If there are lots of spots you may have chickenpox.

Chickenpox is caused by a virus and it's very easy to catch from other children. At first you feel hot (see page 4) and unwell. You get itchy red spots on your face and body. After a few days you get scabs on the spots. Don't scratch them off or they may leave scars. In a week or so you will feel much better.

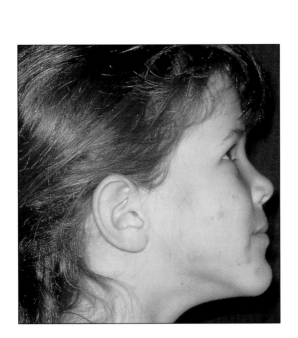

Chickenpox spots cover most of the body and are very itchy.

Measles can also give you a nasty rash and make you feel ill. You may have had an injection when you were a baby to stop you catching measles.

If your skin is very itchy all the time and is also red, dry and scaly, you may have eczema. If you scratch your itchy skin you will make it very sore. You should go to the doctor. He or she can give you creams to soothe your skin so it does not itch so much.

Your skin

Your skin is very important. It helps to protect your body from harmful bacteria. It keeps your body warm but also makes sure it does not get too hot. Your skin is covered with hairs, except on the palms of your hands and the soles of your feet.

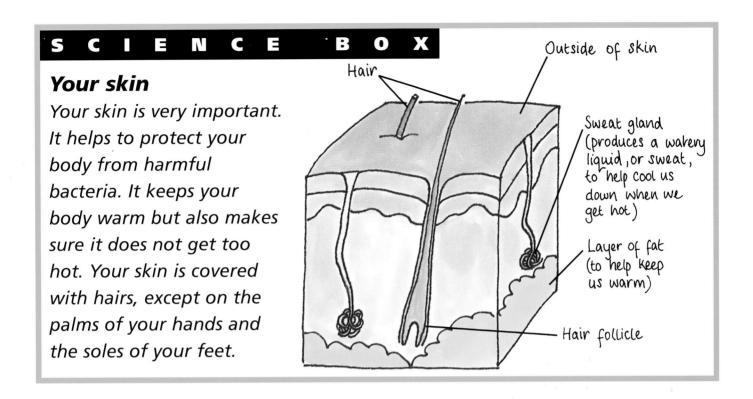

Hair

Outside of skin

Sweat gland (produces a watery liquid, or sweat, to help cool us down when we get hot)

Layer of fat (to help keep us warm)

Hair follicle

Help yourself

Take care of your skin. Keep it clean, eat healthy foods and drink lots of water. Don't burn your skin in the sun. Always put sunblock on your skin when you play in the sun even if you don't think the sun is very bright.

Am I out of shape?

Do you worry that you might be fat? It's more important to think about how healthy you are. Do you hate running around doing sports at school? Do you lie in bed a lot or laze around the house? If you do you may be out of shape. You can be out of shape even if you are thin.

Help yourself

If you eat the right foods and get plenty of exercise you should keep healthy. You should also find it quite easy to stay about the right weight for your height. Your doctor can tell you what is the healthiest weight for you to be.

Eating foods which contain a lot of fat or sugar can make you overweight or tired so try to choose healthy foods more often.

Chicken has less fat than pork or beef. Fish is very good for you. It does not have a lot of fat and it has calcium to make your bones strong. Milk also has lots of calcium and vitamins.

Try to eat more fruit and vegetables. They are even better for you when they are raw.

Exercise helps your body to use up the fat that forms when you have eaten too much. Running around so that your heart beats faster than it does when you are resting will keep your heart and lungs healthy. You will feel more lively, and you may even have more fun!

SCIENCE BOX

Your heart and blood

Your heart is pumping blood around your body all the time, along many kilometres of tiny tubes. The blood carries important substances (taken from the food you eat and the air you breathe) all around your body to give you energy and help you grow. It also takes things your body doesn't need to your kidneys which help to get rid of them (see also page 5).

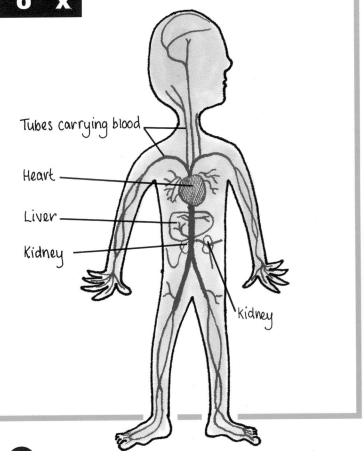

Tubes carrying blood

Heart

Liver

Kidney

Kidney

I've hurt myself

If you hurt yourself, you should tell your mum or dad or someone who looks after you. You need to find out how badly you are hurt.

A cut should be cleaned. If dirt gets into the cut, it can get infected. You may need a plaster on it to help keep it clean. A deep cut may need to be stitched up by a doctor or nurse. It doesn't take long.

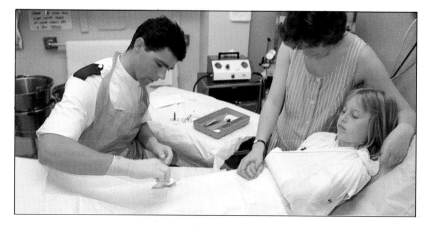

If you hurt yourself badly, you will need to go to hospital.

If you burn yourself, perhaps on your finger, run the cold tap and hold the burn under the water for ten minutes. If you burn a lot of skin, get help straight away. You will need to go to hospital.

Have you ever broken an arm or a leg? It hurts a lot. If you fall and cannot move part of your body, try and keep still. Get someone to fetch help. You will need to see a doctor or be taken to hospital to find out what you have done.

Your bones

Bones are living things. They need vitamins and calcium to grow and be strong. All the bones in your body join up to make your skeleton. The bones meet at joints which allow your bones to move so that you can bend, stretch and jump.

If you break a bone, you will have an X-ray taken. This is a photograph of your insides and will show how and where the bone is broken. A broken bone will usually mend itself over a number of weeks but you will probably have to wear a plaster cast to keep the break still while it mends.

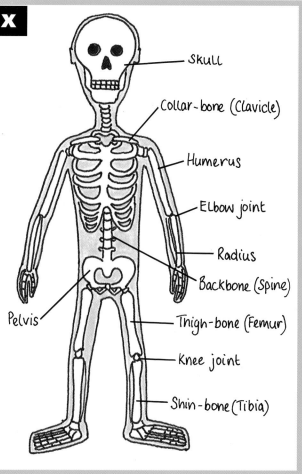

- Skull
- Collar-bone (Clavicle)
- Humerus
- Elbow joint
- Radius
- Backbone (Spine)
- Pelvis
- Thigh-bone (Femur)
- Knee joint
- Shin-bone (Tibia)

Help yourself

You can't avoid all accidents, but you can help to protect yourself. When you ride a bicycle, for example, always wear a crash helmet. If you are using rollerskates or a skateboard, wear a helmet and knee and elbow pads.

When you are playing, think about what you are doing. Always try to do things in the safest way!

I'm having an operation

Sometimes you need to have an operation to put things right inside your body. When you go into hospital for an operation you will find other children there, too. Some may be having the same operation as you.

You may have to stay in hospital for a little while, but there will be toys and things to play with. Your mum or dad or someone who looks after you can visit you any time you like. They may be able to stay at the hospital with you. You can take your favourite toys and books.

Your stomach must be empty when you have your operation, so you'll miss a meal or two. A doctor or nurse will give you a drink to make you sleepy. Then you will be put on a hospital trolley and pushed along to the operating room.

You will be fast asleep when you have your operation. You won't know anything about it. You will wake up back in bed as if nothing has happened, but you may feel a bit sore. You may feel sleepy and thirsty for a while after you wake up. Don't drink or eat too fast.

After some types of operation you have to stay in hospital for a few days. You will soon feel much better and want to get out of bed and play with the other children.

There are lots of things to play with and do if you have to stay in hospital for a little while.

Help yourself

It's not silly to feel scared. Everyone gets frightened. Tell the doctors or nurses how you feel. They will be able to explain things to you. Sometimes they can draw pictures or give you books to help you understand what is happening.

Dial 999

Do you know what to do if someone has been hurt badly?

Do not run away. If there are no adults about, phone for an ambulance. Dial 999. This is a very important number. You should use it only when someone badly needs help straight away.

Someone will answer and ask you which service you want. Tell the person you want an ambulance. Give your name and the address and say what has happened. Listen to what the person says. You may be asked to do something. Do it as quickly and calmly as you can.

Don't be scared. The ambulance should come very quickly. When it arrives, open the front door so the ambulance people can get in.

Help yourself

There are a number of things you can do to help avoid bad accidents in your home.

Fires can kill people or hurt them very badly. Do not play with matches or start a fire. It is a good idea to have smoke alarms in your home to warn you if a fire starts.

Never touch electric sockets and always be careful around things that work by electricity, such as the toaster.

Keep away from bottles that contain substances used for cleaning things. They have poison in them. Do not open containers that are kept in the bathroom cupboard. They probably have medicines in them, and these can be dangerous.

Do not get into the bath if there is nobody about. You could slip and hurt yourself badly, and there wouldn't be anyone around to help. Do not play with the taps. The water could be very hot and burn you.

Glossary

allergic rhinitis An illness in which such things as animal fur, feathers or dust make the nose run and the eyes itch and water.

asthma An illness that makes breathing difficult and causes wheezing and coughing.

bacteria Microbes, some of which can cause illness or damage your teeth.

contact lenses Small lenses which are worn over the pupils of eyes. Like glasses, they help people to see better.

doctor A person who tries to make ill people better.

eczema An illness that causes flaky, sore and itchy skin.

fluoride A chemical that keeps teeth strong.

hayfever An illness in which pollen makes the nose run and the eyes itch and water.

infection Someone has an infection (or is infected) when they have an illness caused by microbes.

inhaler A device used by people with asthma to help them breathe in medicines for their illness.

joints The parts of the body where two bones meet.

measles An illness caused by a virus which produces a high temperature and lots of spots over the body.

microbe A tiny living thing you can see only with a microscope. Bacteria and viruses are microbes.

mucus A thick liquid in the nose and chest.

nerves Like tiny wires carrying messages between the brain and the rest of the body.

operation When a doctor makes you better by changing something inside your body.

phlegm Another word for mucus.

plaster cast A bandage used to protect broken bones. It is hardened with plaster of Paris and wrapped around the broken part of the body; usually an arm or leg.

pollen Part of a plant which looks like dust. Pollen gets blown about in the air.

swollen Has become larger than normal.

temperature The hotness or coldness of something.

thermometer A device for measuring temperature.

viruses Microbes, some of which can cause illness.

Books to read

Going to the Doctor (pop–up book) by Stacey Strong (Child's Play International, 1991)

My Body (Kingfisher Encyclopedia, 1992)

The Human Body Atlas by Mark Crocker (Oxford University Press, 1991)

The Usborne Young Scientist: Human Body by Susan Meredith, Ann Goldman and Tom Lissauer (Usborne, 1983)

Useful addresses

Junior Asthma Club
National Asthma Campaign
Providence House
Providence Place
London N1 0NT
England

National Eczema Society
4 Tavistock Place
London WC1H 9RA
England

Index